On the edge

The sound of danger

Trevor Millum

Folens

© 2003 Folens Limited, on behalf of the author.

United Kingdom: Folens Publishers, Apex Business Centre, Boscombe Road, Dunstable, LU5 4RL.
Email: folens@folens.com

Ireland: Folens Publishers, Greenhills Road, Tallaght, Dublin 24.
Email: info@folens.ie

Poland: JUKA, ul. Renesansowa 38, Warsaw 01-905.

Editor: Kay Macmullan
Layout artist: Suzanne Ward
Cover design: Duncan McTeer
Illustrations: Josephine Blake

First published 2003 by Folens Limited.

British Library Cataloguing in Publication Data. A catalogue record for this publication is available from the British Library.

ISBN 1 84303 390–9

Contents

The story so far

If you haven't read an *On the edge* book before:
The stories take place in and around a row of shops and buildings called Pier Parade in Brightsea, right next to the sea. There's Big Fry, the fish and chip shop; Drop Zone, the drop-in centre for local teenagers; Macmillan's, the sweet and souvenir shop; Anglers' Haven, the fishing tackle shop; the Surf 'n' Skate shop and, of course, the Brightsea Beach Bar.

If you have read an *On the edge* book you may have met some of these people before.

Phil Johnson: *his mum runs the fish and chip shop with Phil's step-dad Ken.*

Mick King: *always bunking off school. His dad runs a local nightclub.*

So, what's been going on?
After Mick and Phil 'borrowed' an old boat and sailed it round the posh marina, Phil was grounded. But that was last summer, this is autumn, and Phil's mum has let him see Mick again. There haven't been any problems. Well, not yet …

What happens in this story?
That would be telling! However, let's just say, Mick has another idea. And this time it involves the old pier. Sounds like danger, Phil thinks.

1

Mick has an idea

Phil and Mick were walking along
the promenade.
"You off home?" asked Mick.
"Yeah," said Phil.
"Coming out tonight?"
"Where?"

Mick was silent for a bit, then said, "I
know a good place."
"A good place for what?"
"Just for looking round."
"I dunno," said Phil.
"It's not nicking stuff or anything," said
Mick, "just exploring."
"Exploring ..." said Phil – more to
himself than to Mick.
It was a word they hadn't used for a
long time.

"Where?" he asked.
"Alexandra Pier. You know, the old pier."

Phil stopped.
Alexandra Pier?
It had been old even when their parents
were kids.

Basically, it was falling into the sea, and there were 'Danger' signs all over it.
No one in his right mind would go there.
But then, Mick wasn't in his right mind, was he?
Phil wasn't sure.

"What are you worried about?" said Mick. "Your mum telling you you're a naughty boy?"
Phil didn't reply.
He didn't even know how they would get on to the pier.
After all, it was rusty and crumbling into the sea.

But he was interested.
There wasn't much else to do, and he didn't want Mick to think he was scared.
"All right," said Phil.
"Meet you outside Mel's after."
'After' meant 'after tea', 'after supper', after whatever else had to happen in the meantime.
It meant, roughly, an hour and a bit.

2

Opening time

Back at the fish and chip shop in Pier Parade, the first customers were waiting for the six o'clock opening.
They were mainly local people at this time of year, as the summer season had recently ended.

Phil pushed his way past them, and came in through the side door.
The familiar smell of hot oil wafted through the kitchen.

Phil's mum raised her eyebrows as he entered.
"Come straight home from school, did you?"
"No. Mick and I had to stay behind."

"You mean you had a detention?"
Mrs Johnson asked, lifting the first
container of chips out of the fryer.
"No. Mick did. And I kept him company."

"Well, now you're here, you can help me
out. Take these keys. It's the big one."
She handed him a large set of keys.
"Go and let those hungry customers in."

Phil walked over to the main
customer door.
He unlocked it.
The waiting line of people entered the
shop and queued at the counter.

At that moment, Phil's step-dad, Ken,
came in from the kitchen.

"Sorry I'm late, love. The cash and carry
was packed. It took me ages to get out."
He gave Phil's mum a peck on the cheek,
and took her place at the fryer.

Mrs Johnson moved to the counter, and
took off her frying apron.
"Yes, sir, what can I get you?"

Phil hovered in the background.
He knew she wasn't keen on him
going out.

He tried to think of what he could tell her.
She wouldn't want him to go anywhere
near the old pier.

When the first customers had been
served, Phil took his chance.
His mum was restocking the stand-up
fridge with drinks, hurrying to get it
done before the next wave of customers
came in.

"Mum – I'm seeing Mick tonight, if that's
OK. I might be a bit late."
"Haven't you got any homework?"
"No – two of our teachers were away."
This was true, as it happened.

Phil's mum thought about it.
She would rather he stayed in, but he was getting to a difficult age.
She couldn't wrap him up in cotton wool.
And she was happier if he was with someone she knew rather than hanging about with strangers.

Mick wasn't an angel but she knew him – and better still, she knew his mum.
She knew his dad too, but he wasn't often around.

"All right," she said, returning to the counter, "but I want you in by nine-thirty.
And when I say nine-thirty – when do I mean?"
"Nine-thirty," he sighed.

He didn't really mind.
Nine-thirty was fine with him.
Perhaps he and Mick wouldn't have time to explore the old pier.

"Can I have some chips, Mum? I'm starving," he said.

"Go on then," she replied, shovelling some into a bag. "And make me and Ken a cup of tea when you've finished."

Phil grinned as he went into their own kitchen, behind the shop.
His step-dad looked sideways at him.
Phil avoided his glance.

The problem with Ken was he always knew when you were up to something.
His mum was always suspicious, but Phil could usually get round her.
His step-dad was a different matter.
But Ken didn't say anything.

Once, when he had, Phil had shouted at him, saying, "You're not my father!"
Now Ken tended to keep quiet.
But Phil still felt guilty.

3

The old pier

It was getting dark when Mick and Phil
arrived at the point where the pier met
the shore.

The pier seemed to stretch a long way out
to sea.
What remained of it was decaying.
The entrance, with its high roof, seemed
sad and neglected.
The paint was peeling, and the metal
supports looked rusty and unsafe.
The railings were high, and there were
strands of barbed wire running along
the top.

There was a large sign reading
'DANGER. UNSAFE STRUCTURE'
nailed to the gate.

The gate was secured by a slack chain and a padlock.

Mick pushed against it.
The gate opened and then stopped.

The chain was taut – but there was plenty of space to squeeze through on to the first platform.

Phil hesitated.
Mick looked at him.

"Scared, Phil?"
"'Course not," he replied.

"What're you waiting for then?"
"Supposing someone sees us?"
"Look, there's no one around."

Further along the promenade a couple
were walking, arm in arm, but they had
their backs to Mick and Phil.
Cars were driving past, but they were
forty or fifty metres away, and seemed
more concerned with getting home, or
wherever they were headed.
A man was walking his dog, but he didn't
seem to be interested.

Mick led the way to the first building on
the far side of the platform.
This had once been the gateway to the
amusements and shops on the pier.

For a moment, Phil thought he could still
hear the sounds of the games, and the
voices of the people.
Perhaps it was just the wind.

All the windows were boarded up,
or broken.
Shards of glass lay on the rickety
wooden platform.
Through the slats, Phil could see the grey
waves breaking on the shoreline.
It seemed a long way down.

The entrance to the main building
was unlocked.
Once again Mick led the way.

Inside, they could hardly see.
He set off along a dim corridor, which
must have once divided the arcades.
Then he stopped, unable to find his way.

Phil walked into him.
"Phil!"
"Sorry. Just don't stop so sudden."
"I'll get myself some brake lights
for you!"
"How do you know where to go?"
"Been here before."

They passed through another door and
came out into a much bigger space.

Perhaps this was the old concert hall,
where entertainers of the forties and
fifties used to play.
There was a small amount of light
– enough to make out shapes as their eyes
got used to the gloom.

"OW!"
"What's up?" whispered Phil. "Are
you hurt?"
"No, I always say OW when I'm enjoying
myself, you idiot!"
"What happened?"
"Walked into something."

Mick rubbed his shin.
"Something wooden, I think. A crate, a
box – I dunno."
"We need a stick. You know, like a blind
person – so we don't walk into things."

"Right," said Mick. "Next white stick you
see, pick it up."

4

Back at the shop

Back at the chip shop, his mum was edgy.

"I'm worried about him, Ken. He shouldn't be out wandering the streets. I should have checked where he was going."

A voice from the kitchen answered her. "He'll be all right."

Ken always said that.
Well, mostly it was true – but it wasn't much help.
Ken didn't want to say what he really thought.
"It's all very well for you. But it's different when it's your own," said Phil's mum.

"Boys get up to all sorts," said Ken.

"That's what I'm afraid of."

"He'll be in soon. Look, I've got to – "

"But he's out with that Mick – and you know what he's like."

There was a rattle of crockery and a rush of water from the tap.

"He's just like all the other lads, isn't he?"

"Well, I wouldn't leave my handbag lying about, put it that way. In trouble at school for bullying. That sort of thing …"

She looked at her watch again.

5

Exploring

Phil and Mick crept further into the
musty building.
It seemed to go on for ever.

Weird shapes rose on each side of them.
Old amusement machines, perhaps,
covered in canvas sheets.
Overhead, somewhere, were steel girders.

It wasn't as interesting as Phil had hoped.
And he kept on thinking about the
sea below.

The pier was definitely swaying, and
several times he had put his foot through
rotten floorboards.

"Where are we going?" he asked.

"We're exploring, Phil. You know – like those blokes in history? Livingstone and them?"

"They had hundreds of servants – and they didn't do it in the middle of the night."

"Don't be such a wimp. If you ..."

He stopped suddenly.

"What's up?"
"Shhh. Listen."
They both listened.

"It's voices," said Mick.
"How can it be?"
"Look, we're here, aren't we? So someone else can be."
"No one in their right mind would be here."
"You said it."

They listened again.
Phil thought he could hear something – then he felt sure he was imagining it.

Then, they both heard.
The same voices as before.

"It *is* voices," whispered Mick. "Coming from over there."
"Where?"
Mick didn't reply.

Phil was ready to turn round and get out of the place.
What was the point of staying anyway?

"I'm going closer," said Mick. "I can see a glow."
Phil didn't move.
He didn't want to go any further – and he didn't want Mick to either.

"It might be …"
"What?"
"Well, you never know …"
He didn't like to say what was in his mind.
If he was honest, he was scared.

"Goblins? Trolls? Witches? Ghosts of old sailors? Go on, Phil. Spit it out."
Phil said nothing.

"Stay here then," growled Mick.
Phil didn't know if it was an order or a put-down.

Mick moved off into the gloom.
There was a glow, somewhere ahead.

Phil watched Mick begin to disappear.

Then there was a movement and a shout.
"Yow. Get off!"
It was Mick.
He sounded surprised.
More unusually, he sounded afraid.

"Got 'im!" said a voice – an old, smoky voice.
Then there was another voice in the darkness.
"Bring him over. Let's 'ave a look-see."

Phil stood dead still.

He listened and he watched but he did
not dare to move.

He could see vague outlines but
little more.
One of the figures had Mick in an
arm lock.
The other grabbed him by the hair, jerked
his head back and stared into his face.

Very slowly and very carefully, Phil
backed away.

6

Under the spell

The woman's face, wrinkled and yellow, peered at Mick.

"Oh, very nice."
"Let go of me!"
"No one here to help you, sunshine. No one except us and the rats," croaked the other figure.

"And Gumbo."
"And Gumbo, of course ..."

Mick managed to speak in a voice that was almost normal.
"Who are you?"

"Didn't we introduce ourselves? Oh,
sorry, dear. Meet Big Sal."
Big Sal spoke.
"And this is Janey. Filthy Janey."

Janey smiled, and the sight was horrible.
A few yellow teeth are worse than none
at all.

"And over here ..." said Janey,
"... is Gumbo."
She indicated a pile of rags in the corner.

Mick could just make out something that
looked like a body.

"Oh yes," went on Janey. "You want to
watch him. He's hard."
"Had a hard upbringing, see," said
Big Sal.
"Wasn't brought up. Wasn't even
dragged up."
"Just sort of burst up."
"Like a weed through the pavement."
"A thistle."
"A dirty big spiky 'orrid thistle."

"Who are you?!" Mick shouted.
"We just told you!" said Janey.
"Wassamatter kid – you deaf?" croaked
Big Sal.
"What?" he croaked.

Janey put her face close to Mick's ear.
Big Sal put hers next to his other ear.

"DEAF?" they roared.

Then, one after another, they shouted the
letters "D, E, F!"

Mick didn't attempt to correct
their spelling.
Instead, he tried to wriggle away.
But Big Sal's grip was too strong for him.
Her fingers were bony – but they were
like metal grips.

He stopped struggling.
He tried to speak calmly.

"I mean … what are you doing here?"
"What are we doing here? Well, we might ask what you are doing here, sonny. And seeing as your wrist is in my fist – maybe you should tell first, eh?"
"Nothing," said Mick.

"No one's doing nothing," breathed Big Sal.
"Even Gumbo's breathing. Just."
added Janey.
"Even the fish's swimming."
"Even the dead's decaying, sonny Jim."

Mick stammered, "I mean – I'm just here. Just exploring. Just …"

Janey mimicked him, "Just, just, just …"
"Cute," said Big Sal.
"Sweet!" said Janey.
"Just, just, just too sweet."
"Bless his little woolly socks."

"I bet his darling mummy don't know where he is."

"Out all hours."
"It'll be in the paper."
"Missing boy."
"Mystery disappearance."
"Comb the streets."
"Search the parks."
"Call the coastguard."

Mick burst out, "I'm not doing any harm.
Let me go! I won't tell."

He could not work out what they wanted.
They weren't like anyone else he had met.
For the first time in his life he felt in
real danger.

"Won't tell?" said Big Sal. "Won't tell
what, cutie?"
"Nothing … nothing."

He couldn't cope with these people.
They really didn't care what they did
– and they certainly didn't care
about him.

"He's crying," said Big Sal.
"Aah. What a shame. Bring him by
the fire."
"Give him a cuddle."
Janey cackled.
"Give him to Gumbo to cuddle!"
"Find him lying in a puddle."
"He'll be in a fine old muddle ..."
"Talking of puddles ... He's wet himself."

Mick managed to speak.
His voice was loud but unsteady.
"Who are you? Who are you?"

They leant close to his face again, but this
time they whispered.
"We're witches."
"Sea witches."

"No such thing," he said.
The grip on his arm tightened and pain
shot through him.
"Yow!"

Janey repeated quietly and with menace,
"We're witches."

7

Going for help

It was almost ten when Phil burst in.

"Phil – where've you been?"
Phil's mum was cross – but she was
also relieved.

"On the old pier."
"The old pier? The one that's crumbling
into the sea?"
She looked at Phil as if he were mad.

"I know, I know, Mum – I was stupid. But
you've got to listen," said Phil. "It's Mick
– he's in trouble ..."

Phil's mum wasn't listening.
She was still trying to take in what he
had said.

"Alexandra Pier?" she said. "The one that's got a sign saying 'Unsafe' on it?"

"Please listen, Mum. You have to help. Help Mick!"
"What've you been up to?"
His mum was paying attention now.

"Nothing. Nothing wrong, I mean."
Phil's step-dad, Ken, was listening.
He didn't say much but he spoke now.
"Come on, Phil."

"Well, you know, just exploring."
"Trespassing," said his mum.
"All right, trespassing – but that's all. Just looking round."
"Looking round? It's not a flipping museum."
"We were just … looking round. We saw these – I dunno, tramps, I suppose …"

His mum looked confused.

"Men? Women?"
"I dunno what they were. Anyway, they got Mick."
"They can have him."
"Mum!"

"What do you mean 'got him'?" asked Ken.
"They just got hold of him and wouldn't let go! We've got to do something."

Phil's mum sighed.
"We can't just leave the shop. It'll be our busiest time in a moment!"
"Please, Mum. This is serious. Put a sign up – say we'll be back soon! Anything."
"I think we should call Mick's mum," she said.
"Or the police," Ken added.
"No. You don't understand. There isn't time. Mick's in danger!"

Eventually his mum gave in.

"All right … but you can make up for this by helping Ken out for the rest of the week with the frying. And we'd better not lose any of our regulars, or you'll be in hot water … or should I say 'oil'?"

"OK, Mum, OK. I've got the message. But we must go now. Bring your phone," he said, moving towards the door. "We can call the police, or Mick's mum, if we need to – but let's go now!"

8

Mick helps out

"Now then, cherub, feeling warmer?"
asked Janey.

She turned to Mick, who was sitting on
the floor next to a smouldering fire in a
metal bin. "Still sniffling?"

"It's the smoke."

"Getting in your poor little eyes, is it?"
asked Sal.

"The smoke don't get out proper. And if
the smoke can't get out, what chance have
you got?" croaked Janey.

"I got in," he said, sullenly.

"But it's a kind of one-way street. One
way for some, anyway."

"What's left of you might find its way
out. Through the cracks."

Big Sal laughed.

"You're mad!" cried Mick.

Janey looked at him.
Then at Big Sal.
"We're mad. Hear that, Sal? Walks in here out of nowhere, crying and wetting himself, and says we're mad."
"Let me go. You're hurting. It's not fair!"

Janey looked over at the pile of rags in the corner.
"Gumbo would like things fair, wouldn't he?"
"He would. A bit of fair play would suit him grand."
"Tell you what, let's get our little friend to cheer poor Gumbo up."
"Yeah," said Big Sal. "Entertain him."
"Sing him a song. Eh, sonny?"

"I don't know any songs," said Mick.

"Oh you do, sonny. Everyone knows songs – and you're gonna sing."

9

Looking for Mick

Down by the promenade, the few street lamps did not give out much light.

Phil, his mum and Ken approached the chained gate.
"Lucky we're not fat," said Ken as they squeezed through.
He was trying to be cheerful.
Phil's mum didn't see much to be cheerful about.

"What on earth made you come in here?" she asked.
"It's only an old pier," was all Phil could say.

Phil's mum looked down at the sea crashing on the stones below.

Even here, the wood felt rotten, and the pier seemed to sway.
However, they crossed the platform and made their way through the entrance hall, using Ken's torch.

Suddenly, Phil stopped.
"Shhh. Listen."

Very faintly they could hear the sound of singing.
"Oh I do like to be beside the seaside, Oh I do ..."

"I don't believe it," whispered Phil.
They crept closer.

Ken switched off the torch as the glow from the fire became clearer.
There was no doubt – Mick was singing.

"Oh I do like to be beside the sea!
Oh I do like to ..."

Ken stepped forward.

"Who's there?" called Janey.

All three of them walked into the glow of the firelight.

Mick looked around, saw there was nothing to stop him – and got up.

Big Sal and Janey suddenly looked smaller and older.

Janey spoke in a meek, quavery voice, "You his dad?"

"Er, his friend's dad. Sort of," said Ken.

"Glad you could find us," said Big Sal.

"Such a nice boy," said Janey. "So polite."

"And kind," said Sal.

"Mick?" gasped Phil's mum.

"Oh yes," said Janey. "When he found out – you know, how we was fixed. Making the best of it here. How poor old Gumbo was homeless and helpless and couldn't get nothing. 'Cos he's got no address. Hardly got a name."

"He just set to. You know, to cheer him up. Found out what we like best," went on Big Sal.

"Yes, an old song. We like that. Reminds us of better days. We had to teach him first though."
"And he sang to us."
"I don't believe it," said Phil, quietly.

"He's brought a little joy into our lives tonight, haven't you, Mick?"
Mick didn't answer.
He was dazed.
It all felt like a dream.
What was he doing on this stupid old pier?

"Well, we'll have to take him home now … It's …"
"Late. Of course. Should be tucked up in bed!"
Janey smiled a horrible smile.

They turned to leave, but first Ken put something into Janey's hand.

"Er, take this. Just to help out, like."
"You're very kind," she said. "Just like
our Mick."

Big Sal looked at Mick.
"Do come and see us again. Any time!"
She laughed.

To Mick it was a dreadful cackle.
To the others it was just a laugh.
A tired, old laugh.

They made their way slowly out, crossing
the platform and wooden boards back to
the entrance.

Looking back, the pier seemed
almost unreal.
Like an old, grey snake stretching out
to sea.
A snake ready to crumble into pieces and
melt beneath the waves.

10

End of the evening

They got into the car, and headed back down the seafront.
It was only a short drive back to the fish and chip shop.

"Do you think they'll be all right?" asked Phil's mum.
"We can phone someone when we get back," said Ken.

It was a quiet journey home.
Mick was silent.

Phil was tempted to ask him for a song – but he didn't.

As for Mick, he couldn't get that song out of his head.

'Oh I do like to be beside the seaside.
Oh I do like to be beside the sea!
Oh I do like to walk along the prom prom prom.
Where the brass bands play tiddley om pom pom.'

At that moment, 'beside the sea' was the last place on earth Mick wanted to be.